GRAPHIC SCIENCE

EXPLORING ECOSYSTEMS

WITH

MAX AXIOM
SUPER SCIENTIST

www.raintreepublishers.co.uk

Visit our website to find out
more information about
Raintree books.

To order:

☎ Phone +44 (0) 1865 888066
▤ Fax +44 (0) 1865 314091
▣ Visit www.raintreepublishers.co.uk

Raintree is an imprint of Capstone Global Library Limited, a company incorporated in England and
Wales having its registered office at 7 Pilgrim Street, London EC4V 6LB
Registered company number: 6695882

"Raintree" is a registered trademark of Pearson Education Limited, under licence to Capstone Global
Library Limited

Text © Capstone Press 2008
First published by Capstone Press in 2008
First published in hardback in the United Kingdom by Capstone Global Library in 2010
The moral rights of the proprietor have been asserted.

ISBN 978 1 4062 1464 2 (hardback)
14 13 12 11 10

British Library Cataloguing in Publication Data
Biskup, Agnieszka.
Ecosystems. -- (Graphic science)
577-dc22
A full catalogue record for this book is available from the British Library.

Art Director and Designer: Bob Lentz and Thomas Emery
Cover Artist: Tod Smith
Colourist: Matt Webb
UK Editor: Harriet Milles
UK Production: Alison Parsons
Originated by Capstone Global Library
Printed and bound in China by South China Printing Company Limited

Acknowledgements
The publisher would like to thank the following for permission to reproduce copyright material:
Corel p. 17

CONTENTS

5

Organisms need energy to live. Based on how they get energy, living things can be divided into three groups.

These groups include producers, consumers, and decomposers.

Most producers are plants.

Plants make their own food from sunlight through a process called photosynthesis.

A closer look shows that plants use the sun's energy to change water and carbon dioxide into a simple sugar.

CARBON DIOXIDE

OXYGEN

ENERGY

WATER

SUGARS

The sugar is a form of stored energy called glucose.

DEFINITION

nutrient substance needed by a living thing to stay healthy; plants get nutrients mainly from the soil in the form of minerals; animals get nutrients mainly from the foods they eat

Consumers that eat plants for energy are called herbivores.

This group includes tiny insects and larger animals, such as deer.

Of course, not all consumers eat plants.

Carnivores eat other animals to get energy. This group includes sharks, lions, hawks, and wolves.

Omnivores eat both plants and animals for energy.

Grizzly bears are omnivores. They eat grasses and berries, as well as salmon.

Rats, crows, and humans are omnivores too.

But even the hungriest animals leave leftovers.

Scavengers, like vultures, crabs, or seagulls, are always ready to clean up. They get energy by eating the bodies of dead animals.

Decomposers get energy from breaking down the remains of dead plants and animals even more.

Bacteria and fungi are decomposers.

They help break down the flesh and bones of dead animals so plants and other living things can reuse them.

DID YOU KNOW?

Without decomposers and scavengers, the world would be full of the remains of dead plants and animals. As nature's recyclers, decomposers are a necessary part of an ecosystem.

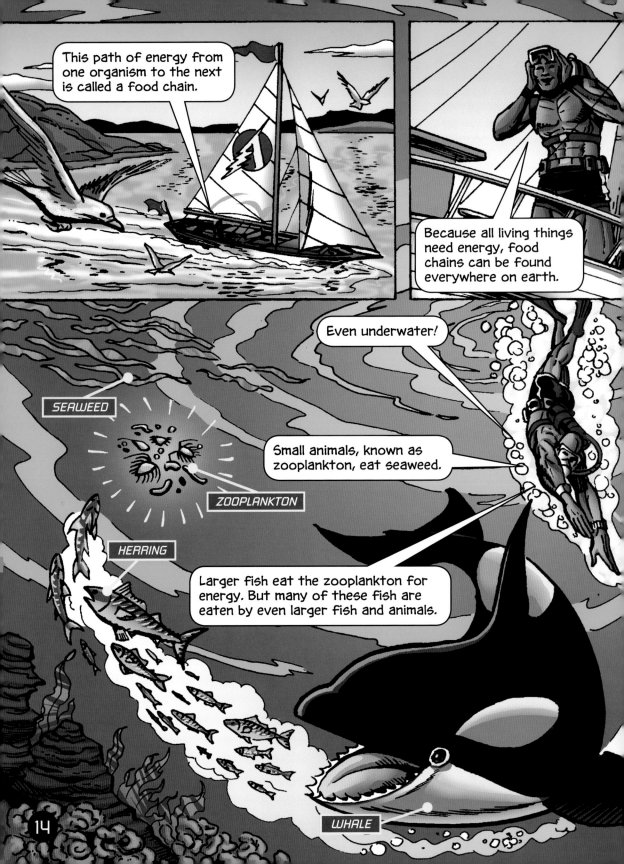

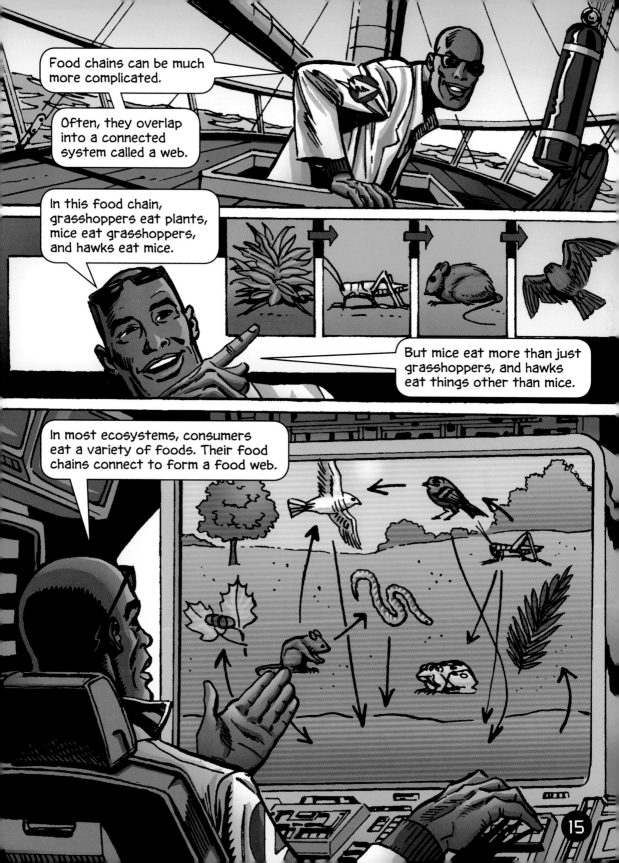

Food chains can be much more complicated.

Often, they overlap into a connected system called a web.

In this food chain, grasshoppers eat plants, mice eat grasshoppers, and hawks eat mice.

But mice eat more than just grasshoppers, and hawks eat things other than mice.

In most ecosystems, consumers eat a variety of foods. Their food chains connect to form a food web.

The sun's energy flows through ecosystems in one direction. Other elements are reused or recycled.

Water is reused in two ways.

When oceans, lakes, and rivers are heated by the sun, water turns into vapour.

Water vapour in the air gets cold, changes into liquid, and forms clouds. The air can only hold so much water.

When clouds get too heavy, water falls back to the earth as snow or rain.

Most of this precipitation falls back into the ocean or runs off land into lakes or streams.

And the cycle begins again.

DEFINITION

precipitation water that falls from clouds to the earth's surface; precipitation can be rain, hail, sleet, or snow

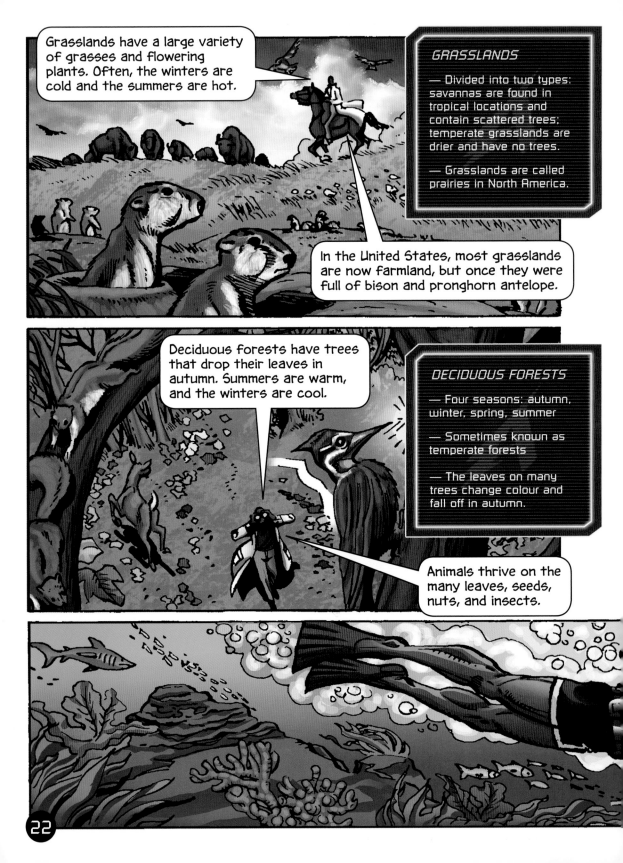

Grasslands have a large variety of grasses and flowering plants. Often, the winters are cold and the summers are hot.

GRASSLANDS

— Divided into two types: savannas are found in tropical locations and contain scattered trees; temperate grasslands are drier and have no trees.

— Grasslands are called prairies in North America.

In the United States, most grasslands are now farmland, but once they were full of bison and pronghorn antelope.

Deciduous forests have trees that drop their leaves in autumn. Summers are warm, and the winters are cool.

DECIDUOUS FORESTS

— Four seasons: autumn, winter, spring, summer

— Sometimes known as temperate forests

— The leaves on many trees change colour and fall off in autumn.

Animals thrive on the many leaves, seeds, nuts, and insects.

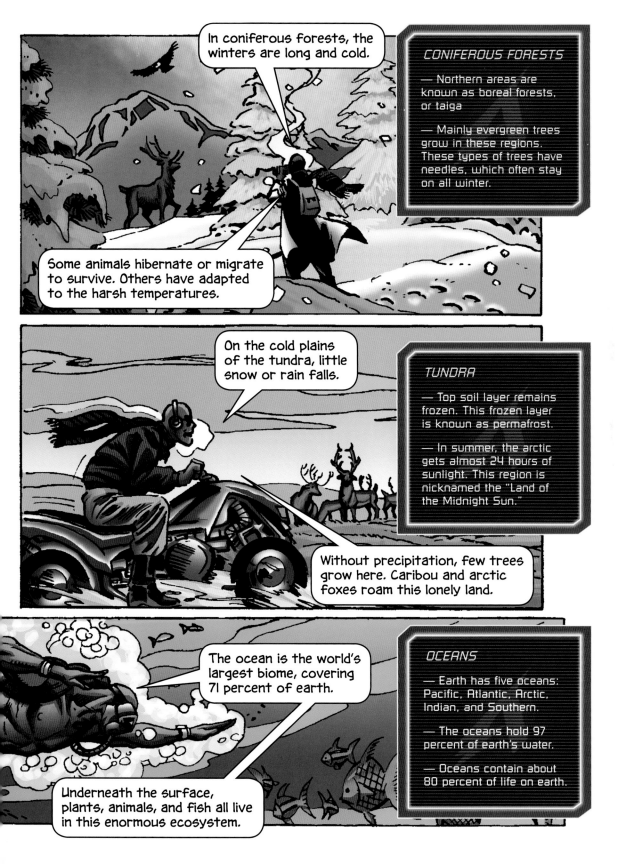

In every ecosystem, the relationship between plants, animals, and their environment is a delicate balance.

When one part of an ecosystem suffers, the other parts are often affected.

In Canada and the northern United States, the population of snowshoe hares directly affects the number of lynx.

One year, hares are everywhere!

But few lynx roam the land.

Long ago, mountain lions and wolves balanced deer populations. But humans eliminated many of these natural predators.

Today, deer numbers have risen in the United States. Overpopulation leads to lack of food. The hungry deer mow down plants and trees, which may never come back.

Humans also change the face of earth by cutting down forests, turning grasslands into farmland, and building on wetlands.

Unfortunately, these changes are not always for the better.

REDUCE YOUR IMPACT

You can protect the earth's ecosystems by practising conservation. Use fewer natural resources such as water and gas. Reduce waste and pollution whenever possible. Recycle bottles, cans, paper, and other recyclable materials.

MORE ABOUT ECOSYSTEMS

Ecosystems can be as large as an ocean or as small as a fishbowl. To identify the many ecosystems, some are called after their main feature, such as a pond ecosystem, a salt marsh ecosystem, or a rainforest ecosystem.

Ecosystems are fragile, and alien invasive species can be a major problem. These plants and animals have been introduced to a part of the world where they don't belong. The brown tree snake was originally from Australia and Indonesia. Somehow, this sneaky reptile slithered onto a plane and hitched a ride to the island of Guam. With few predators on Guam, the tree snake has nearly wiped out the native forest birds.

Believe it or not, the extinct passenger pigeon was once amongst the most numerous animals on earth. In the early 1800s, the passenger pigeon population was estimated at 1 to 5 billion birds. Huge migrating flocks actually darkened the sky when they passed. Largely due to over-hunting, the pigeons began to decline. By the 1890s, only small flocks were left. The last passenger pigeon died in a zoo in 1914.

In the early 1990s, scientists tried to reproduce the ecosystems of the earth inside a 1.4-hectare (3.5-acre) building called Biosphere 2 in Arizona, USA. The building contained a desert, a rainforest, and even a 4,000,000-litre (900,000-gallon) ocean. Some scientists believed buildings like Biosphere 2 could support life on the Moon or Mars. But after only two disappointing missions inside, the experiments ended.

The rainforest is one of the largest biomes on earth. Sadly, more than 0.6 hectare (1.5 acres) of rainforest are destroyed every second.

People should do their bit every day to protect the environment. Special days throughout the year help us to remember this important task:

Earth Day (22 April) – celebrates clean air, land, and water

World Environment Day (5 June) – encourages environmental awareness worldwide

MORE ABOUT

Real name: Maxwell Axiom
Height: 1.86 m (6 ft 1 in.)
Weight: 87 kg (13 st. 10 lb.)
Eyes: Brown   Hair: None

Super capabilities: Super intelligence; able to shrink to the size of an atom; sunglasses give X-ray vision; lab coat allows for travel through time and space.

Origin: Since birth, Max Axiom seemed destined for greatness. His mother, a marine biologist, taught her son about the mysteries of the sea. His father, a nuclear physicist and volunteer park warden, showed Max the wonders of the earth and sky.

One day, while Max was hiking in the hills, a megacharged lightning bolt struck him with blinding fury. When he awoke, he discovered a new-found energy and set out to learn as much about science as possible. He travelled the globe studying every aspect of the subject. Then he was ready to share his knowledge and new identity with the world. He had become Max Axiom, Super Scientist.

GLOSSARY

carbon dioxide colourless, odourless gas that people and animals breathe out

community populations of people, plants, or animals that live together in the same area and depend on each other

ecology study of the relationships between plants and animals in their environments

environment the natural world of the land, water, and air

mate to join together for breeding

offspring animals born to a set of parents

organism living plant or animal

population group of people, animals, or plants living in a certain place

recycle process of turning something old into something new

transpiration process by which plants give off moisture into the atmosphere

FIND OUT MORE

Books

100 Facts on Rainforests, Camilla de la Bedoyere (Miles Kelly Publishing, 2008)

Carbon-Oxygen and Nitrogen Cycles (Earth's Processes series), Rebecca Harman (Heinemann Library, 2005)

Changing Ecosystems, Michael Bright (Heinemann Library, 2009)

Predicting the Effects of Climate Change, John Townsend (Heinemann Library, 2009)

The War in Your Backyard: Life in an Ecosystem, Louise and Richard Spilsbury (Raintree, 2006)

Websites

www.wwf.org.uk
Visit the World Wild Fund for Nature's website to find out what steps are being taken to protect endangered species and their habitats.

www.envirolink.org
The website provides up-to-date news and information on the environment.

INDEX